A BITE Inside

Karen Ball • Jon Stuart

Contents

OXFORD
UNIVERSITY PRESS

Macro Marvel
(billionaire inventor)

Welcome to Micro World!

Macro Marvel invented Micro World – a micro-sized theme park where you have to shrink to get in.

A computer called **CODE** controls Micro World and all the robots inside – MITEs and BITEs.

A MITE

A BITE

Disaster strikes!

CODE goes wrong on opening day.
CODE wants to shrink the world.

Macro Marvel is trapped inside the park ...

Enter Team X!

Four micro agents – **Max, Cat, Ant** and **Tiger** – are sent to rescue Macro Marvel and defeat CODE.

Mini Marvel joins Team X.

Mini Marvel
(Macro's daughter)

In the last book ...

CODE key
(12 collected)

- Mini found her dad inside Marvel Towers, but he was not well.

- Mini and Rex were trapped by MITEs.

- Team X made a plan to shrink and fly inside Macro Marvel!

You are in the Marvel Towers zone.

3

Before you read

Word alert

- Which is the tricky part in each of these words?

  wrist   rhythm

- Which letters make the /r/ sound in these words?

  wrinkling   rhubarb   rose

- Look out for other words that include the /r/ sound when you are reading.

What does it mean?

> brow – forehead

Into the zone

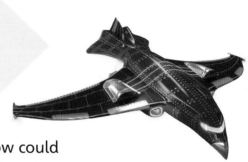

- What do you know about Hawkwing?
- What does an X-ray show you? How could Team X and Mini use one to help them?

4

A Micro Plan

Team X stood in the Micro World Control Room. They had shrunk to micro-size. Above them, they could see Mini trapped between a MITE and Macro Marvel.

Ant put on his X-ray glasses. He could see what Marvel had eaten for breakfast: porridge and rhubarb. He saw Marvel's lungs going up and down in a steady rhythm. The BITE was lurking nearby.

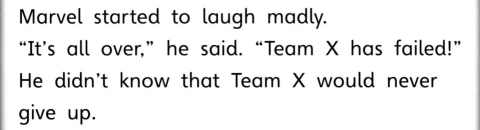

Marvel started to laugh madly.
"It's all over," he said. "Team X has failed!"
He didn't know that Team X would never give up.

Suddenly, Marvel opened his mouth wide and began to sneeze. The BITE inside him was making him ill.

"Let's put our plan into action," said Ant. The plan was to shrink to nano-size and fly inside Marvel's body using Hawkwing. Cat was not convinced.
"I don't know about this," she said, her brow wrinkling.
"Come on, Cat. We'll be okay inside Hawkwing," said Max.
Max pulled the craft out of his backpack and they began to shrink it.

Team X pressed the buttons on their wrist watches and shrank to nano-size. Soon they were tiny enough to fit inside Hawkwing.

They scrambled into the craft and Max and Ant wriggled into the drivers' seats.

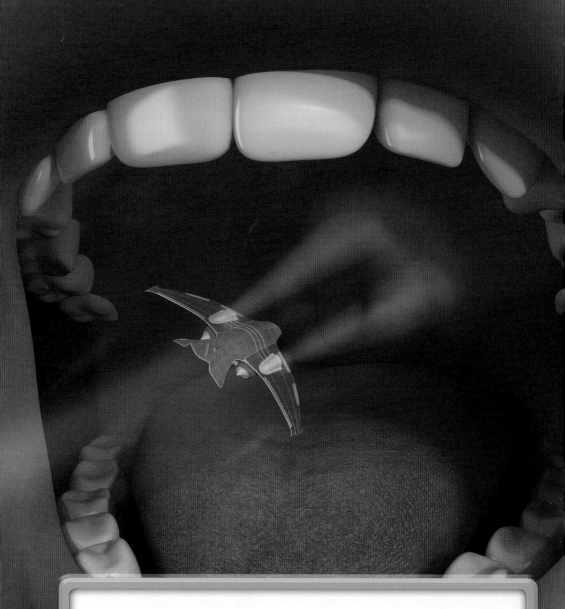

Hawkwing rose up as Marvel opened his mouth to sneeze. Max and Ant steered the craft into Marvel's mouth, which snapped shut behind them.

Now you have read ...
A Micro Plan

Word swap

Look back at page 7. It says that
Macro Marvel laughed 'madly'.

Try using a different word to
describe how he laughed.
How does that change the meaning?

Imagine

Imagine you are with Team X and are
flying into Marvel's mouth. What do
you think it would be like?

Say, think, feel

Can you remember what Cat said about the plan?
What did she think of it? How did she feel?

Before you read

Word alert

- Look at the words. Here is the sound to remember when you are reading this story:

wrong   **wr**iggle

wrestle   **rh**ythm

- Look out for more words with this sound when you are reading.

What does it mean?

gradually – happening slowly, a little bit at a time

fire extinguishers – containers of foam or water used to put out a fire

Into the zone

- Can you remember where Mini and Rex are? How did they get trapped?
- Does Mini know what is wrong with her dad?

14

Mini Fights Back

Chapter 1 – Under Control

Marvel had no idea he'd swallowed Hawkwing!
He picked up Mini's Gizmo.
"I'll keep this," he said, his voice cold.
"Dad! What's wrong with you?" Mini asked.
Mini had never seen her dad like this. She
didn't know there was a BITE controlling him.

Marvel didn't answer Mini's question. Instead he looked over at the MITEs.

"Lock her up!" he ordered. "She must stay here until CODE has shrunk everyone in the world. We must keep people safe!"

Mini was shocked. Didn't her dad realise that CODE had gone wrong? She tried to wriggle free to speak to him but the MITEs were too strong.

Mini couldn't talk to her dad. Marvel had fallen asleep and was slumped in his chair. His eyes were closed, his chest rising and falling with the rhythm of each snore. The BITE inside Marvel's body was making him ill and tired. Mini's Gizmo lay loosely in his hand.

"I have to get it back!" she thought.

Mini was too late! One of the MITEs scuttled over and scooped up the Gizmo. The MITE put the Gizmo into a safe in the wall. Mini watched the MITE punch in the numbers: 8, 9, 7, 11. With a loud click, the safe locked.

The MITE marched Mini towards a small room. Rex tried to fly after her. Before he could reach her, the other MITE grabbed Rex by the leg and chained him to Marvel's chair.

Mini watched helplessly from the locked room.

"I have to get my Gizmo back," she thought. "How can I get it now?"

Chapter 2 - Escape

"Rex, what are we going to do?" Mini cried. Rex lifted his head and let out a stream of fire. Gradually, the heat began to melt the chain that held him to the chair. "Clever Rex! Keep going!" Mini said, clapping her hands together with delight.

As clouds of smoke rose up into the air, the MITEs ran towards some fire extinguishers in a corner of the room. Jets of white foam spurted from the fire extinguishers, and soon the MITEs were slipping and sliding across the floor.

Rex flew over to the room where Mini was locked up. There was a flash of orange as more flames shot from Rex's mouth, melting the lock.

The door swung open and Mini was free! She stepped out and hugged Rex. "Well done, you were terrific!" she said. "Now let's get my Gizmo back."

The MITEs were soon back on their feet and racing towards Mini. She quickly ran towards the safe. Rex breathed a jet of fire and the MITEs staggered back.

Marvel was still sound asleep. This was Mini's chance to rescue her Gizmo ... if only she could remember the numbers for the safe!

Chapter 3 - The Numbers Game

Mini stared at the safe.

"What buttons did the MITE press when it locked my Gizmo away?" she muttered to herself.

Mini thought hard and then a smile spread across her face. Fortunately, she had inherited her dad's good memory. She suddenly remembered that the last two numbers rhymed.

"8, 9, 7, 11," she repeated as she quickly punched in each of the numbers.

There was a click and the door of the safe swung open. Mini reached inside and grabbed her Gizmo, clutching it to her chest.

The MITEs saw Mini take the Gizmo and moved towards her. They caught Mini and tried to wrestle the Gizmo from her.

Suddenly, the MITEs began to fizz and pop and then they stopped working! Mini quickly wriggled free.

"The foam must have got into their circuits," said Mini. "Now I can contact Team X."

Now you have read ...
Mini Fights Back

Rex's story
How did Mini and Rex escape? Talk about the three things Rex did, using the pictures to help you.

True or false?
Are these sentences true or false?
Use evidence from the story to explain why.

- Mini's dad is usually friendly.   True   False
- MITEs don't give up easily.   True   False
- Mini has a bad memory.   True   False

Think about the story
Why do you think Mini was so desperate to get her Gizmo back?